Inside the Earth

by David Orme

Inside the Earth

by David Orme
Educational consultant: Helen Bird

Illustrated by Stefan Lindblad

Published by Ransom Publishing Ltd.
51 Southgate Street, Winchester, Hants. SO23 9EH
www.ransom.co.uk

ISBN   978 184167 804 7

First published in 2009

Inside the Earth

Contents

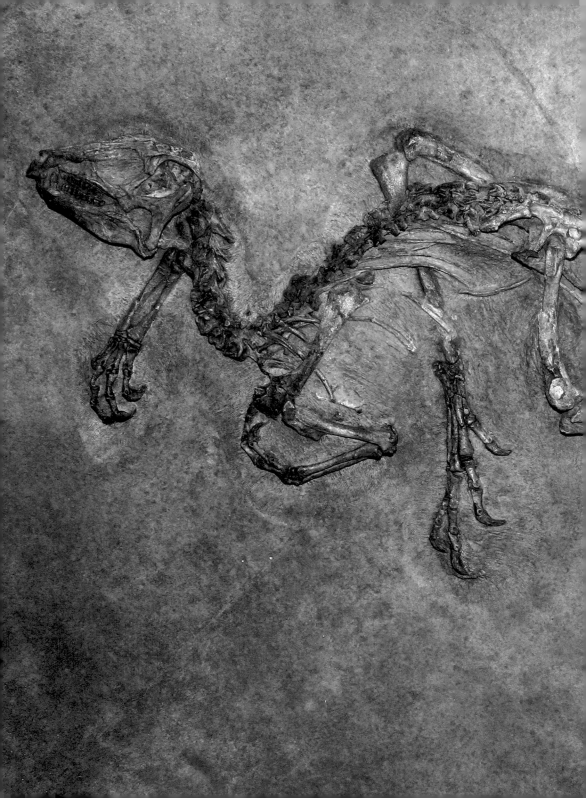

Inside
the Earth

Get
the
facts

Caves

How are caves made?

Some caves are made when water gets into cracks in the ground and dissolves the rock.

Sea caves are made when the sea wears away a cliff.

Ice caves can form inside glaciers.

Caves made by water can be very long, and very big.

Troll Blazers

Mammoth Caves, Kentucky, U.S.
The world's biggest cave system.

Water trickling through the rocks makes amazing rock formations.

Stalactites and stalagmites

Stalactites hang **down**.
Stalagmites grow **up**.

Which is which?

Remember: stalactites hold **tight** to the roof.

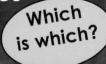

7

People in caves

People have used **caves** for their **homes** for millions of years.

Broken pots, bones, fireplaces and even **paintings** have been found in caves.

Sometimes, people were buried in caves. The '**Red Lady**' was buried 30,000 years ago in a cave in **Wales**. Her bones were coloured red.

Only problem – 'she' turned out to be a man, not a lady!

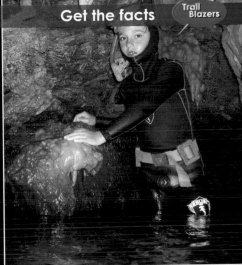

Cave diving

Exploring caves isn't always easy. If a cave is full of water, only **divers** can explore it.

This can be **dangerous**. Many people have died diving in caves.

Amazing tunnels

Some early tunnels were built to carry water.

Tunnel building really got under way with canals and railways. Canals and railways can't climb hills!

This tunnel is on the island of **Samos**, near **Greece**. It is over 1 km long.

It was built around **2,500 years ago** by **slaves**. They started digging the tunnel from each end.

Somehow, they managed to meet in the middle – no one is sure how they managed it!

The **Seikan Tunnel** in **Japan** – at 33.5 miles, it is the longest tunnel in the World.

The **Thames Tunnel**. The first tunnel in the World that went under water. It took nearly 18 years to build. It is still used by trains.

Living underground today – underground cities.

Montreal, Canada, has its own underground city. It has shops, offices, even places to live! The tunnels stretch for 32 km.

Why live underground?

- It's cool in summer and warm in winter – it saves energy.

- In countries that are very cold in winter, with lots of snow and ice, living underground makes sense!

- You are not affected by the weather.

This underground house is in **Coober Pedy, Australia**, where it is very hot. It makes a cool place to live!

Burials

Most cultures of the world bury
dead people underground.

Most bodies are buried in a grave
dug into the ground.

This can be a problem when there is no
more room! In London, in the nineteenth
century, the **churchyards** were **very small.**

Tens of thousands of bodies were stuffed into
them. Bodies were often dug up again after
a few weeks to make room for more bodies.

Important people were buried
under the floors of churches.

Ancient burial mound at
Anundshög, Västerås, Sweden.

The space under a religious building is called a **crypt**. This was often used as a place to put bodies.

When large numbers of people died, maybe because of **war** or **plague**, bodies were often buried in **huge pits**.

This happened in **London** during the **Great Plague** of 1665.

Underneath this boring-looking car park in London are the bodies of **thousands** of **plague victims**.

Digging up fossils

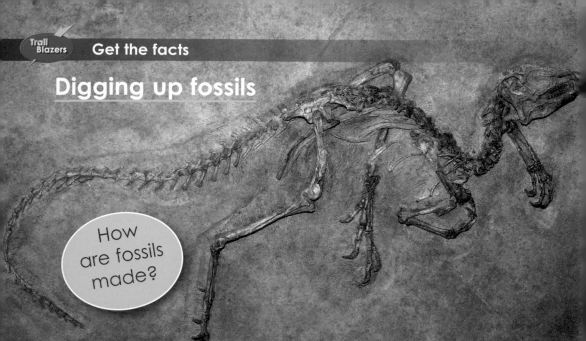

How are fossils made?

When an animal or plant dies, it might be covered with mud or soil.

As it rots away, the space is filled with other materials that take its shape.

After a long time, these other materials become the fossil.

Sometimes other traces of animals can become fossils. This **dinosaur footprint** is 167 million years old.

Dinosaurs

A T Rex.

People have been digging up dinosaur bones for thousands of years, but no one knew what they really were.

Some people thought they were the bones of dragons!

Dinosaur bones are very rare. Keep digging – you may be lucky!

A Triceratops.

Journey to the centre of the Earth

A movie poster from 1959.

In 1864, the writer Jules Verne wrote a story called Journey to the Centre of the Earth.

His heroes went into a volcano. They thought they could get to the centre of the Earth.

Did they? **No.**

Could they? **No.**

In fact, they couldn't go down that far at all!

The **deepest** that people have gone into the Earth is **nearly four kilometres**, in a **gold mine** in **South Africa**.

The temperature down there is 55 degrees.

A gold mine.

The deeper you go, the hotter it gets! Deep down, the Earth is liquid metal. This is called the mantle. In the centre of the Earth, there is a core of rock. This may be over 5,000 degrees!

The Earth's interior

Mantle

Inner core

Crust

But people still like writing stories about strange goings on deep in the Earth ...

Chapter 1:
The narrow tunnel

John had worked as a porter at the station ever since the railway had come to the town in 1838.

Every night, when he finished work, he walked to his home, two miles away on the other side of the hill.

It was hard work climbing the hill after a long day's work, so after the last train John took a short cut – through the railway tunnel.

John the porter had finished work for the day. It was a long walk home ...

One winter night, John set off home as usual. It had been raining all day, and the tunnel was damp. A cold wind blew through it.

This was one of the first railway tunnels ever built. It was narrow, almost too narrow, and only the smallest engines could pass through.

No one had thought about building safe places for people to stand when trains went through.

Chapter 2:
The extra train

John was half way along the tunnel when suddenly he heard something terrifying – the beating sound of a steam engine coming into the tunnel ahead of him!

John looked around desperately. But there was nowhere he could go to get out of the way of the engine.

There was only one hope. John stood in the middle of the track, and waved his lantern towards the train.

But would the driver see it in time?

An extra goods train was running that night. On the engine, the driver and fireman were finding it hard to see through the smoke in the narrow tunnel.

'Joe, put on the brakes!' yelled the fireman. 'There's a light waving on the track.'

Joe shut off steam and put on the brakes, but it was too late. The brakes wouldn't grip on the wet track.

There was no escape for John. The train hit him full on. He was killed instantly.

Chapter 3:
The light

A hundred and fifty years later, trains had stopped running through the tunnel. The station had closed, and the line was taken up.

The ends of the tunnel had been closed up with wooden boards, but people had come along and pulled them down.

One summer day two boys, Wayne and Chris, decided to explore the dark, damp tunnel.

Waynes's torch lit up the tunnel. Here and there, bricks had fallen from the crumbling roof – it looked dangerous.

But the boys didn't want to show they were afraid. They walked on.

'Hey, Chris, what's that light?'

'Maybe it's the other end of the tunnel.'

'Can't be. It's boarded up.'

'Wayne – there's someone in the tunnel!'

Chapter 4:
Who was he?

A man was rushing towards them, waving an old-fashioned lantern. His face was staring at them, terrified, but it didn't speak.

'Let's get out of here, quick!'

The boys turned and ran, stumbling across the fallen bricks.

The entrance to the tunnel was a bright circle ahead of them. But before they got there, they heard a sound behind them – a rumbling noise, like the sound of a steam engine clattering along the rails!

'Chris! It's a train!'

'Can't be. There are no rails!'

They got to the open air. The rumbling turned to a roar behind them and choking dust poured out of the tunnel.

When the noise stopped and the dust died down, the boys went back to the tunnel and shone their torches into it.

Just inside, they saw a great pile of bricks and earth. The crumbling tunnel had collapsed.

'If we hadn't got out, we would have been killed.'

'That man with the lantern. He warned us! But who was he?'

(This story is based on a true story of the Canterbury to Whitstable railway in the U.K.)

Inside the Earth word check

canal	mantle
churchyard	plague
crust	Pompeii
crypt	stalactite
Edinburgh	stalagmite
formations	T Rex
fossil	temperature
glacier	Triceratops
Great Plague	tunnel
inner core	volcano
lantern	